C000135378

MYTH AND MAGIC
OF
NORTHUMBRIA

**SANDHILL
PRESS**

First published by Sandhill Press in 1992, reprinted 1996.

This book incorporates some material first published in 'Ghosts &
Legends of Northumbria', ' More Ghosts & Legends of
Northumbria' *published in 1989 and* ' Customs and Traditions of
Northumbria' *published in 1991, all the copyright of Sandhill Press.*

© Sandhill Press Ltd.
17 Castle Street, Warkworth,
Morpeth, Northumberland, NE65 0UW

ISBN 0 946098 45 X

Myth & Magic of Northumbria: retold by Sandhill Press.
Designed by Sandhill Press, set in Palatino 10pt.

Cover illustration © Sandhill Press,
with cover artwork by Linda K.
Graphic Design Studio, North Shields.

Printed by Clifford Press Ltd., Coventry.

Enter the world of
mystery and imagination through these
pages. Here you will encounter fairies
and witches, brownies, bogles and brags,
dragons, vampires and a host of other
fantastical creatures.
Stories traditionally told around firesides,
ballads sung by minstrels, associated with well-
known places in Northumbria are retold here for
your entertainment.

BEWARE!! - perhaps these creatures still exist?

CONTENTS

THE CAULD LAD O' HILTON
❖•❖•❖•❖•❖•❖•❖•❖

Hilton Castle, in the valley of the River Wear, near Sunderland, was visited around the beginning of the seventeenth century, by a noisy little imp of the 'Brownie' type. A 'Brownie' was thought to be an unembodied spirit which had never lived in human form, and many of our old castles and houses were said to have been visited by them.

This particular 'bar guest' or local sprite, was heard but rarely seen, by the servants at Hilton Castle, who became so used to his nightly jinks, they were not afraid of him. If they left the kitchen clean and tidy before retiring for the night, the little goblin took great delight in hurling the dishes and pots and pans around, causing general havoc and confusion. Alternatively, if they left the kitchen in a state of disorder, the 'Cauld Lad' would tidy everything away, leaving the room remarkably clean. Naturally the servants took advantage of this, and rarely tidied up at night.

However, after a while, the servants grew tired of this nightly disturbance, and followed the tradition of leaving a tasty bite to eat, or an article of clothing, to banish such a sprite away from a house. Aware that the servants planned to banish him, the goblin could be heard chanting these words:

> *"Wae's me, wae's me*
> *The acorn is not yet*
> *Fallen from the tree*
> *That's to grow the wood*
> *That's to make the cradle*
> *That's to rock the bairn*
> *That's to grow a man*
> *That's to lay me."*

They had a small green cloak and hood made up for the 'Cauld Lad' and laid it out in front of the kitchen fire. Having settled to watch the imp's reaction, on the stroke of midnight he duly appeared, gliding into the kitchen, and inspecting the gifts left for

5

him. Delighted, he tried them on and danced around the kitchen, admiring himself. As dawn broke, and the cock crew, the sprite disappeared, saying:

"Here' s a cloak and here's a hood,
The Cauld Lad o' Hilton will do no more good."

Indeed, he was never seen again in the Castle, but at midnight a mournful disembodied voice could often be heard singing the above lines.

Although the 'Cauld Lad' was thought to be of the 'Brownie' type, he has been identified with the ghost of a young stable boy, Roger Skelton, who was accidently killed by one of the Barons of Hilton at the end of the sixteenth century. The Lord, having ordered that his horse be saddled and ready at a certain time, grew impatient, strode into the stables and, finding the stable boy asleep, struck him a fatal blow with a hay fork. Horrified by his act, the Baron covered the boy with straw and later that night threw the body into a nearby pond.

Many years later the skeleton of a boy was removed from the pond. The records of the Coroners Inquest of 3rd July, 1609, show that the boy was accidently killed by the point of a hay fork. The Baron was later pardoned in September of the same year.

If the 'Cauld Lad' was the ghost of the boy, it is strange that he was so relatively harmless, when the stable lad had met with such a horrific death. Many thought, however, that it was his ghost that was heard singing verses from the ballad entitled 'The Cauld Lad o' Hilton:

"Hilton's line dishonoured fall;
Lay with the dust proud Hilton's walls.
Murder blots the household sword;
Strip the lands from Hilton's lord..."

The sprite at Hilton was also said to row people across the Wear in a ferry boat, tethered near to the Castle. Sometimes he would take them only half way and then disappear, leaving the passengers to fend for themselves, reappearing later to row them to the original landing place.

6

THE HEDLEY KOW

+•+•+•+•+•+•+•+•+•

The 'Hedley Kow', a mischievous rather than malevolent 'boggle', haunted the village of Hedley, near Ebchester, in County Durham. Whenever he played one of his tricks on someone, he always ended his mischief with a raucous laugh at their fear or amazement of his pranks.

An old woman gathering sticks at the side of the road, would find a truss of straw lying in front of her. Naturally, the woman would be tempted at the sight of this, and would pick it up and add it to her bundle. However, her load would then become so heavy, that she could no longer carry it, and laying it down, would be amazed to see the 'truss of straw' dancing and swinging from side to side down the road in front of her. Kicking his heels and snapping his fingers as if in time to a tune, the Hedley Kow would laugh and disappear.

He also liked to play tricks on courting couples. One night as two young men set off to meet their sweethearts, they thought that ahead of them they saw the two girls. However, no matter how fast the two men walked, the girls still remained in front, until eventually, after hearing strange laughter, they found themselves walking into a bog.

They realised the Hedley Kow was up to his usual tricks, and managing to get out of the bog, they ran for home, the boggle following at their heels, shrieking and laughing. Crossing the River Derwent, one of the men fell into the water, the other stumbling after him. Thinking that each was the Kow, they cried in terror and panic as they rolled about, struggling to get out of the water. Eventually they returned home to tell the sorry tale of how they had been chased by the Hedley Kow.

The sprite played many tricks on local farms and farmers. A farmer called Forster got up early one morning to travel to Newcastle, and thinking that he had caught hold of his grey mare in the dimly-lit dawn, he harnessed it to the cart. However, as he stepped up to drive away, the horse kicked up its heels, and neighing loudly, disappeared from the farmyard, another victim of

7

the Hedley Kow's mischief.

The boggle's presence in the district caused much havoc. He sometimes called to sleeping servant girls, pretending to be their sweethearts, and they would stumble eagerly to open the windows and peer out, but, alas, they would be disappointed. Sometimes when the girls were busy elsewhere, the naughty sprite would overturn milk churns and allow the cat to lick the cream. The imp would then unravel their knitting or tamper with their spinning wheels.

Often assuming the shape of a cow, the sprite would lead the milkmaid a merry dance around the field until he finally allowed himself to be caught. He would kick and misbehave throughout the milking and would then upset the milk pail, slipping his rope to give a loud bellow before running off, letting the girl know that she had been tricked by the Hedley Kow. It is thought that it was from this prank that the boggle got its name.

Although the sprite did not visit houses in mourning, he certainly liked to be present if a birth was imminent. As the anxious father-to-be rode for the midwife, or Howdie, the Kow would tease him by appearing in a lonely place, making the horse stand absolutely still, neither the whip or the spur being able to move it. If the farmer was allowed to reach the Howdie without incident, and settle her beside him on the horse, the imp would appear just as they were passing through a stream. He would then cause the horse to kick and rear, depositing the unfortunate couple in the water.

Sometimes as the wife lay in pain waiting for the midwife, the Kow would come to the door or window and mock her. As the farmer rushed out with a stick to attack the imp, he would find the weapon removed from his hand and turned upon his own shoulders. Often after chasing the pest around the farmyard, the unfortunate farmer would trip over one of his own calves, unable to gain his balance, before the Kow disappeared.

Eventually, the local people were so used to being victims of the Kow's mischief, that they expected to fall foul of him in certain places. Riding home late one night, a farmer approached a lonely stretch of road which was known to be one of the Kow's haunts. Seeing another rider ahead of him, he quickened the horse's pace in order to have some company for the rest of the journey. However, the rider in front, hearing the increased pace behind him, spurred his own horse and set off at a gallop.

The two rode at terrible speed for about two miles, until the man behind called "*Stop! Stop!*" The man ahead, hearing noises but unable to distinguish the words, finally decided to confront his pursuer. "*In the name of the Father and of the Son, and of the Holy Ghost, who art thou?*" Instead of being mocked by what he obviously thought was the Kow, his terrified neighbour replied "*Aa's Jemmy Brown o' the High Fields. Who's thou?*" This amusing tale was related by Stephen Oliver in his book '*Rambles in Northumberland*'.

The following incident illustrates how seriously people believed in the Hedley Kow at this time. Thomas Stephenson, of Framwellgate Moor, Durham, gave a sworn statement to Mr. Justice Burdess in 1749 stating that on the night of 17th August, 1729, between eight and nine o'clock, journeying from Hedley to Durham, he was suddenly faced with a strange apparition.

Continually changing its form from a man to a foal, it finally seized the bridle of Stephenson's horse, wrenching it from the animal's head, and proceeded to beat both Thomas and his guide until they were very sore, leading their horse in another direction, and totally confusing them. Eventually Stephenson found the bridle tied around his waist, but his horse remained under the spell of the phantom until dawn, when it vanished. It was later found on Green Bank Top, one of the Hedley Kow's favourite haunting places.

Ben Jonson's lines, concerning Robin Goodfellow, also provide an apt description of the Hedley Kow:

"*Sometimes I meet them like a man,*
Sometimes an ox, sometimes a hound,
And to a horse, I turn me can,
To trip and trot about them round.
But if to ride,
My back they stride,
More swift than wind away I go:
O'er edge and land,
Through pools and ponds,
I whirry laughing, Ho! ho! ho!"

BROWNIES, BOGLES, BRAGS & THE LIKE

Brownies, bogles, hobgoblins and sprites were all believed to have haunted our area creating either havoc or carrying out good deeds. These are just a few of the different characters who roamed the northern countryside.

BROWNIES

The type of Brownie found in the Berwickshire area was of the friendly kind and because he was believed to be *"the ordained helper of mankind in the drudgery entailed by sin"*, he could receive no wages for his good deeds. He allowed treats, however, in the form of knuckled cakes made from warm meal from the mill, toasted over the fire and eaten with honey. Housewives would prepare these treats and leave them where the sprites could find them sometimes with their other favourite dish, a bowl of cream. If a household wished to be rid of their 'lodger' they would leave out a new hood for him and he would leave, singing a similar rhyme to the Cauld Lad o' Hilton:

"A new mantle and a new hood
Poor Brownie! Ye'll ne'er do mair good."

RED CAP

The Redcap, Redcomb or Bloody Cap was *"cruel and malignant of mood"* and lived in Border castles, towers and peles, once the scenes of tyranny and bloodshed. In his *'Folklore of the Northern Counties'* Brockie gives a graphic description of the evil sprite:

"He is depicted as a short thick set old man, with long prominent teeth, skinny fingers armed with talons like eagles, large eyes of a fiery red colour, grisly hair streaming down his shoulders, iron boots, a pike staff in

10

his left hand, and a redcap on his head."

If stranded travellers took refuge in the deserted buildings Redcap threw huge stones at them and, if particularly angry, he would murder them, catching their blood in his cap - hence his name.

It was possible to drive out the malicious sprite by quoting words from the Scriptures or by holding up the Cross, he would then *"yell dismally, or vanish in a flame of fire, leaving behind him a large tooth on the spot where he was last seen."*

DUNNIE

This sprite, of the Brownie type, could be found at Hazelrigg, Chatton, in Northumberland and he indulged in mischievous tricks which exasperated the local people. If a midwife was required by a local farmer he would saddle his horse, unaware that the form of the animal had been taken by the Dunnie, and set off to collect the 'Howdie'. Although the 'horse' carried the farmer safely to his destination, on his return journey, the imp would vanish and deposit the unfortunate pair in the mud. Similarities can be drawn here with the Hedley Kow.

Another favourite trick was to take the form of a ploughman's horse and having captured the beast in the field and harnessed him, the man would unhappily see the *"harness slap to the ground"* as the 'horse' kicked up his heels and fled.

It was thought that the Dunnie was actually the ghost of a Border Reiver as he was often heard singing in the Cheviot Hills, in a melancholy voice:

> *"Cocken heugh there's gear enough,*
> *Collier heugh there's mair,*
> *For I've lost the key o' the Bounders,*
> *An' I'm ruined for evermair."*

TRICKERY AT CALLALY CASTLE

❖•❖•❖•❖•❖•❖•❖•❖•

The present Callaly Castle, near Whittingham in Northumberland, was built in 1727, but the remains of a medieval building can still be seen on top of Callaly Castle Hill nearby. A legend, associated with the original plan to build a castle on this site in the twelfth century, illustrates a crafty deception which succeeded because of the superstitions and beliefs of the time.

It seems that many arguments took place between the Lord and Lady of Callaly over the building plans. The Lord wanted his new castle on the hill, while his wife preferred a more sheltered site in the valley below. Finally, ignoring her objections, the Lord ordered his builders to go ahead with their work on the hill site.

However, each day the men erected the walls of the new castle, but returned the following morning to find their work destroyed, and the walls pulled down. Because of their fear of the unknown, they naturally assumed that evil powers were at work.

Bravely, the master builder decided to keep an all-night vigil at the site, and settled down in an old shepherd's hut to see what spirits the darkness would bring. Several hours passed uneventfully, until finally, when all was quiet, a strange creature, resembling a boar, appeared. Standing on its hind legs, it began to tear down the castle walls. When all the newly-laid stones were lying at its feet and the destruction was complete, it cried in a loud voice:

"Callaly Castle built on the height,
Up in day and down at night
Builded down in the Shepherd's Shaw
It shall stand for aye and never fa'."

Terrified to hear or see any more, the builder fled.

The following day, the Lord was told of these strange occurances, but, refusing to believe the tale, he vowed to keep watch himself that very night.

Again, as darkness and silence enveloped the quiet

12

countryside, the boar appeared and tore down that day's building stones, and recited the strange verse. Having seen this terrifying creature for himself, the Lord immediately told his wife that he had changed his mind and the castle would now be built on the lower sheltered ground.

She was delighted - her plan had worked! The 'boar' was, in fact, one of her servants dressed in an animal's skin, and playing on the superstitions of the time, she was successful in gaining her wish.

Another version of the story does not mention the boar but states that mysteriously:

"Each particular stone, one by one, rose gradually upon its end, toppled over, and fell noiselessly to the earth. No visible agency was discernible..."

A dismembered voice was still heard, however, emanating from the ruinous heap, saying the above verse.

Callaly is also associated with another superstition concerned with the weather. When the mist rose from the ravine between Castle Hill and Lorbottle Moor, and clung to the top of the hill, local people used to exclaim : *"Callaly pot is boiling!"* - this was a sure sign of rain.

There was also a 'Callaly pot', which the Clavering family, who owned Callaly, used to boil, providing dinner for poor people who attended services on Sundays and holidays, at the chapel attached to the mansion.

Hob Thrush's Mill Nick is a deep fissure with pot holes and waterfalls in Callaly Crags, near Callaly Castle. 'Hob Thrush' was a local sprite, similar to a 'Brownie', and it is reputed that he ground his grain at the 'mills' . They were set in motion by the waterfalls which brought down stones that rattled in the pot holes, making a sound like the grinding gear of a mill.

ENCHANTED HILLS AND FAIRY MUSIC
✠•✠•✠•✠•✠•✠•✠•✠

There can be few children, or adults, who haven't heard stories of fairies; either fairy rings, fairy godmothers, fairies at the bottom of the garden, or the very popular 'tooth' fairy. Indeed, centuries ago when people were more superstitious and inclined to believe in ghosts, demons, witches and the like, these tales were numerous.

The oldest fairy tale is believed to have been written on papyrus in Ancient Egypt for a young crown prince, but we need look no further than our own Northumbria to discover more about these fairy folk.

Small, well-proportioned beings, often with beautiful golden hair, they were said to ride miniature cream-coloured ponies. Little bells were attached to their horses' reins or manes, and it is strange to note that the hooves never left a mark on the ground. The fairies frequently made their homes in the green hills of Northumbria's countryside, living underground. Laying their ears to the ground, people would claim that they could hear pipers playing, and much singing and dancing.

One such 'fairy hill' is believed to have been at Bishopton, in Teesdale, at the old fortress home of the Conyers family, called Castle Hill. Tower Hill, at Middleton-in-Teesdale, is another famous hill, and it is generally supposed that the town of Ferry Hill in County Durham, is a corruption of 'fairy hill'.

An old woman claimed to have seen fairies in Teesdale come down from Tower Hill to wash themselves, and their clothes, in the River Tees. One day, the woman found a fairy, dressed in green with brilliant red eyes, sitting on a small cheese-shaped stone near to her house. She took the miniature girl home with her and sat her by the fire, giving her bread and butter with sugar on it. The fairy ate the bread, but cried so desperately that the woman was forced to return her to the spot where she had originally seen her. However, the woman kept the stone, preserving it as a sacred item, and allowing no one to touch it.

People also claimed that they heard the fairies patting butter on

Pensher Hill as they passed by at night. Once a man heard them say *"Mend that peel!"* (*a peel was a long-handled shovel used to remove bread from the oven.*) Passing by the next day, he found the broken shovel and took it home to be mended.

The following day a piece of bread and butter was lying on a stone where he had found the peel. The man was afraid to eat the bread or give it to his horses, fearing the consequence. Unfortunately, unaware that he had offended the fairies, his horses dropped dead before he reached the top of the hill. (*A certain fungus found at the roots of trees was known as 'fairy butter', as, after heavy rainfall, it formed a consistency and colour similar to butter.*)

There is another interesting mound between Eppleton and Hetton, near Houghton-le-Spring, consisting entirely of stones, at the top of which is a small hole, known as the 'fairies cradle'. Here the fairies would dance to music performed on a magical pipe, played by a ghostly minstrel.

Many people have been enchanted by fairy music, some to their peril. Fawdon Hill, near Whittingham, believed to be the residence of 'Queen Mab' and her elfin courtiers, was the scene of their moonlight dancing and feasting.

"The sun burst on Brandon Hall,
And burnish'd the windows and silver'd the wall,
And the crimson light of morning fell,
On Fawdon Hills, where the fairies dwell.

...The circle is formed and the revels begun.
The queen is its centre, and, bright as the sun,
She sits in her floating pavilion of gold,
Her vassals to honour, their sports to behold.
The graver spirits stand round the throne,
And Puck and the Brownies within the zone.

Ah! happier far with that mortal alone
In the flow'ry vale when the breeze was still,
Than to form a link of the glittering zone
That circled the bosom of Fawdon Hill."

15

Some centuries ago, a farmer was riding past Fawdon Hill at midnight, when he heard beautiful music and silvery laughter. He imagined the sounds were coming from the hill itself, and as he drew closer, an open door in the hill side revealed the fairy court at a wonderful banquet.

As he stood, motionless and spellbound, the fairies saw him. One of the pages approached with a drinking cup, offering it to the frightened and bewildered farmer. The man took the cup, but afraid of its contents, he threw it to the ground and rode off as fast as he could.

Others were not as fortunate. Henhole, a great chasm in the side of the Cheviot, was another headquarters of the fairies. This is a wild, rugged place situated between two crags where a small burn tumbles down the steep slopes, strewn with stones. At one time a party of hunters were chasing after a roe and found themselves led to this lonely spot.

Suddenly they could hear silvery music, but where was it coming from? The chase forgotten, they determined to find the source of the enchanting music. Following the sounds, they eventually entered the Henhole, all except for one man who was afraid of the stony ground. He waited a while, in vain, for his companions. He was to be the only one to return home, the other hunters were never seen again.

Fairies were often seen dancing in the fields at night. Children used to dance around a fairy ring at Chathill, north of Alnwick. They believed that if they danced more than nine times around the ring, some evil would befall them.

A maid who lived near Netherwitton, not far from Morpeth, was returning from her milking one day, carrying her pail on her head, as was the custom. Although they were invisible to her friends, she could see the fairies dancing in a field. When she reached home she discovered a four-leaved clover instead of the usual circular pad, or 'weise', which was placed under the pail to protect her head. It was believed that if anyone had such a charm, it gave them the power to see fairies. It was also thought that such people were evil spirits, disguised as humans, giving instruction to those who practiced magic.

THE ROTHLEY FAIRIES

In Northumbria many of the instances of fairy folklore appear around particular places, such as parts of County Durham, Teesdale, Weardale, the area around Morpeth, including Netherwitton, and, in this instance, Rothley.

These are two tales of encounters with the fairy folk centred in or around this small village. The first was at Rothley Mill, an isolated place, thought to be used by the fairies as a meeting place and a kitchen. It is still possible to see the hollowed out basins near the burn, reputedly made under Queen Mab's orders, to be used as the fairy bathing places.

The mill itself was the fairies' council hall and the eye of the kiln in the kitchen was where they boiled their porridge.

The miller was aware of the other inhabitants of his mill, but usually left them to their own devices. However, he became annoyed with the fairies as they did their cooking on his kiln and often burnt the husks of corn he had laid out to dry, to be ground later. Having cast a spell over the mill, the fairies saw the seed and corn as a reward for guarding the mill against evil.

Deciding that they had taken too much corn, the miller was determined to put an end to their extravagances. One night, as the fairy folk were preparing their supper, the miller climbed on to the roof and threw a sod of earth down the chimney, fleeing quickly from the scene. The earth landed in the cooking pot, showering the fairies with soot and hot porridge.

Furious, they ran after the miller, shouting *"Burnt and scalded! Burnt and scalded! The sell of the mill has done it!"*

The miller ran ahead of the angry fairies but did not manage to escape, as the mother of the fairies caught up with him. She simply touched him and he fell on the spot. The miller limped home, a cripple for the rest of his life.

The second story concerns a widow and her son who lived at Hartburn, near Rothley. The child, who was wilful and disobedient, refused to go to bed one winter's evening when his mother asked him. Eventually, having tried to persuade him by threatening that

17

the fairies would come and take him, the mother went to bed herself, leaving the child sitting by the fire.

He was not alone for long when a beautiful doll-like figure came down from the chimney and stood on the hearth in front of him. The boy was astounded, but the creature was smiling as it walked back and forwards in front of him, and he ventured to ask, *"What do they ca' thou?"* The fairy replied, *"My ainsel"*, and promptly asked the boy the same question. Not wanting to appear outwitted, he answered, *"My ainsel."*

The two then began to play as friends until, the fire having died down, the boy went to stir it with the poker. Unfortunately a cinder fell out onto the fairy's foot and her tiny voice rose to a deafening roar of pain.

The boy ran and hid under his bedclothes as the fairy's mother appeared, demanding *"Who's done it? Who's done it?"* *"Oh, it was my ainsel "* answered her sobbing daughter. *"Why then,"* said her mother, forcing her daughter back up the chimney, *"What's all the noise for, there' s nyen to blame!"*

It was a long time before the boy disobeyed his mother again. It is easy to imagine this story being told many times by mothers in an attempt to make their young children behave!

WITCHES AND WITCHCRAFT
✦•✦•✦•✦•✦•✦•✦•✦•

The hysterical mania against witches which swept Europe, fuelled by both Catholics and Protestants, reached its peak in Great Britain in the sixteenth and seventeenth centuries. Laws were passed during the reign of Henry VIII, not revoked until 1736, whereby imprisonment and death were the punishment for anyone convicted of acts taken to be sorcery or witchcraft. This frenzy of delusion about witchcraft became so virulent that many poor and innocent people were wrongly accused and put to death. The situation was graphically described by Gaule in his *'Select cases of conscience touching witches and witchcraft'* published in 1646:

"In every place and parish, every old woman with a wrinkled face, a furred brow, a hairy lip, a gobber tooth, a squint eye, a squeaking voice, a scolding tongue, having a rugged coate on her back, a skull-cap on her head, a spindle in her hand, a dog or cat by her side, is not only suspected but pronounced a witch. Every new disease, notable accident, miracle of nature, rarity of art, nay, and strange work or just judgment of God, is by the people accounted for no other but an act or effect of witchcraft."

These persecuted old women invariably had a broomstick or two standing in the ingle nook which was taken as further evidence of their being witches. There has always been magic associated with the broomstick, it being believed that the witch would sit astride it and so sail through the air, as alluded to in the following lines by Gay on the 'Old Woman's Complaint'

"the stunted broom the wenches hide,
For fear that I should up and ride"

It was believed that the broomstick maintained its buoyancy in the air by being treated with a magic ointment made from the fat of bodies of children stolen out of the churchyard.

Three thousand persons, judged guilty of witchcraft, were executed in England during this period, independently of those put

19

to death by mobs and after illegal trials.

In Newcastle upon Tyne on 26th March 1649, a petition concerning witches was read to the Council. This resulted in the magistrates sending two of their sergeants, Thomas Stevel and Cuthbert Nicolson, into Scotland to engage the services of the so-called 'Witch-Finder'. On their return the local bellman proclaimed through the streets that anyone with complaints against witches and the like should immediately denounce the persons involved.

Some thirty women were therefore brought to the 'Witch-Finder', almost twenty-seven of whom were found guilty by his method of sticking pins into their limbs and watching for any blood flow. For this service he was paid almost three pounds for each case.

Following their conviction at the Assizes, on a day in August in 1650, fifteen so-called witches and a wizard were hanged on the Town Moor.

One particular case of witchcraft occurred in the neighbourhood of Alnwick in 1682-3, the alleged witch being a woman named Margaret Stothard who lived in the nearby village of Edlingham. She was credited with many extraordinary powers, possibly being a medium, clairvoyant or hypnotist, and became known as 'The Witch of Edlingham.' The charges against her (detailed in Mackenzie's 'History of Northumberland') were laid before Mr. Henry Ogle, the local Justice of the Peace, on 22nd January, 1683.

John Mills, a yeoman of Edlingham Castle, was the first witness. He swore that one night, unable to sleep, he felt a huge blast of wind shaking the house, something fell with a great weight on his chest making a noise like a cat, and the figure of Margaret Stothard appeared, surrounded in light, at the foot of his bed. So terrified was he by this experience that he became subject to frequent fits during which he screamed "The Witch, the Witch". It was necessary to restrain him until the episode passed.

The second witness against Margaret Stothard was William Collingwood, also of Edlingham. He claimed that eight or nine years previously Jane Carr of Lemendon had told him that Margaret had placed a charm on her child to cure some sickness. Apparently this was achieved by Margaret placing her mouth over the child's and "chirping and sucking" as if drawing out the heart from the chest. The child recovered but an animal tethered nearby subsequently

20

went mad and had to be killed. The superstition was that the witch had drawn the sickness from the child and passed it into the animal. *(Today the likely explanation might have been the quite common use of mouth to mouth resuscitation.)*

Jacob Mills from Eglingham Castle told a similar story involving the child of Alexander Nickle of Lorbottle. In this instance Margaret Stothard was supposed to have refused to treat the child. It was reported however, that she had waved a white cloth over the infant three times. When the baby subsequently died it was believed that it had been cursed, especially as no less a person than the well-respected Lady Widdrington, claimed that at the time of the child's death it was not suffering from any illness.

Finally, Isabel Maine, a spinster of Shadow, brought her information against the witch. In service to Jacob Pearson of Titlington, she claimed to have consulted Margaret Stothard when her master's herd began to produce sour milk. She was advised to rub salt and water into the backs of the cows when they were in the byre and always to put a little salt in her milking pail. Apparently the milk did become pure again and both butter and cheese could be made from it.

It would seem, however, that Margaret Stothard, although she accepted no payment for her good advice, had suffered denouncement as a witch as her thanks in the matter.

There is no real evidence as to how this strange affair ended. Perhaps because her cures and good works appeared to outweigh her curses, Margaret Stothard was allowed to die in her bed. Possibly the local population was too in awe of her powers to see her hanged or tortured to death as happened in similar cases.

For further cases of women tried as witches see the accounts which appear in the Publications of the Surtees Society.

The following account of 'The Wallsend Witches' should perhaps be taken with a 'pinch of salt'.

This horrific tale of the gruesome events in Old Wallsend Church was originally documented by Sir Francis Blake Delaval. Somewhat of a *"mystery man and humorist"* Sir Francis, who died in 1771, carefully described the events as happening *"once upon a time"*

21

to a certain *"one of the Lords of Seaton Delaval."* Certainly the experiences described are macabre enough to have ensured that the legend has survived throughout the years.

Delaval, returning home from Newcastle one dark night, was surprised to see the interior of the old church at Wallsend brilliantly lit. Riding up through the grave yard, he dismounted, tethered his horse, and walked forward to look in a window. The sight that met his eyes would have frozen anyone to the spot with sheer terror.

A number of withered hags sat around a communion table at each corner of which an inverted human skull burned incandescently. The horrible creatures were in the process of cutting up the body of a female, which was partly uncovered from a coffin shroud. Amid loud, cackling laughter, one of the witches (described as having a stubbly beard, buck teeth, red eyes and grossly wrinkled skin), tossed a severed piece of body to another crone, who disappeared with it towards the belfry.

Immensely sickened by the scene, Delaval vowed that the foul fiends would burn at the stake for their disgusting deeds. With great courage and disregarding his own safety, he flung himself through the door of the church, and burst in among the grim gathering.

The hags fled, some towards the roof, but Delaval managed to grab and hold on to the chief dissector in whose hand still gleamed a bloody knife. Despite her struggles and curses he managed to secure the weapon and tie her hands firmly behind her back. Throwing the creature over his horse, Delaval bore off his dreadful prisoner to face justice.

Subsequently convicted of witchcraft, she was sentenced to be burnt on the shore near to Seaton Delaval. Even at her execution however, the witch almost escaped justice. For some reason her captors granted her request for the use of two wooden dishes, which were brought from Seaton Sluice. The fire to burn the witch was well established, and as smoke rose from it in dense columns, she placed one foot in each dish, and soared clear of the flames over the heads of the amazed spectators.

However, although it seemed she would escape, at the last moment one of the dishes broke, and she crashed back to earth. She was instantly seized and placed on the bonfire where, engulfed by flames, she perished.

THE HAND OF GLORY
✠•✠•✠•✠•✠•✠•✠•✠

Over the centuries, people have believed in various charms and superstitions used to practice witchcraft or 'dark magic'. One of these, the 'Hand of Glory', introduced into this country from abroad, was a gruesome, severed hand of a hanged man, reputed to have the power to induce deep sleep and so render victims helpless and unable to move.

In his novel, *'The Antiquary'*, Sir Walter Scott describes its preparation:

"The hand has to be wrapped in a cloth - part of a winding sheet - and squeezed of any blood in the veins, then put into an earthen pot with pickling spices and saltpetre, until the hand is mummified. A candle has next to be made with a pitch wax, the fat of a hanged man, 'virgin wax' and mustard oil. The dried, shrivelled hand has to have this candle fixed in its fingers, and lighted; now the charm will work."

Such a hand was used at an old inn on the Bowes to Brough road by a band of robbers. The Old Spital Inn, now a farmhouse, stood in an isolated spot in the district of Stainmore and was owned by George Alderson who lived there with his wife and son, and maid, Bella. One October night in 1797, as they sat close to a roaring fire, a storm raged outside and torrential rain lashed at the shutters. Suddenly their quiet reverie was broken by a great hammering on the heavy oak door. The last coach of the day had been gone for some time, and no other visitors were expected.

On instructions from Alderson, Bella drew back the bar, and opened the door. Light from the room revealed the figure of an aged, bent woman, concealed beneath a large hat and billowing cloak, which were soaked through from the rain. She was invited to enter and warm herself by the fire. Refusing to remove her outer garments, the old woman explained that she was travelling south and would be grateful to sit by the fire until dawn, when she would continue her journey.

The inn keeper and his family retired for the night, Bella,

23

however, was suspicious that all was not as it appeared. The old woman had spoken little, and her refusal to take off her hat and cloak added to Bella's uneasiness. She therefore lay down on a settle near the fire, determined to watch the stranger, whilst herself feigning sleep.

An hour passed until the figure stirred and revealed from beneath the cloak a leg encased in a horseman's gaiter - the 'old woman' was, in fact, a man! Having checked that the maid was asleep, the man took a withered human hand from beneath his cloak and, placing a candle in its palm, chanted:

"Let those who rest more deeply sleep,
Let those awake their vigil keep."

Lighting the candle, he continued:

"Oh, Hand of Glory, shed thy light,
Direct us to our spoil tonight."

The flame grew to a brilliant light as the man unbarred the door and, going outside, gave a sharp whistle to summon his accomplices - it was now obvious that a robbery was planned. Bella, who had been watching this strange ritual, leapt to her feet and threw herself at the man's back, sending him falling into the road. Quickly she ran upstairs to rouse the innkeeper, but neither he nor his son could be awakened : the charm of the Hand had done its work. Realising this, the quick-witted maid ran back downstairs and doused the candle with a bowl of milk.

Moments later, awoken from their deep sleep, Alderson and his son appeared armed with guns and fired at the robbers, one of whom fell, dead or injured. Asking Alderson to hold his fire, the robbers promised to leave if the withered hand could be returned to them. Refusing this request, the father and son fired further shots which finally drove the robbers from the inn. The gruesome 'hand' was said to have remained at the inn for many years, before finally being lost.

24

LEGENDS OF STONES
❖·❖··❖··❖··❖··❖··❖··❖·❖

Not only are there many ghostly stories and strange happenings in our famous houses and castles, and fairies and brownies haunting our moors and hills, the various large stones in Northumbria are also associated with folklore and legend.

One of the most famous of these is the Monk's Stone, a weathered whinstone pillar, surrounded by wooden rails, which used to stand in front of the Monk's House, a farm house, in a field near Tynemouth. At one time the stone was engraved and richly decorated, human faces had been cut into one side, with engravings of two animals above their heads.

The stone was always referred to in legal documents as a 'rood' or 'cross', and is thought to have been set either as a boundary stone between Monkseaton and Tynemouth as a guide to travellers, or used to denote the limit of sanctuary given to the monastery at Tynemouth. Today, the stone stands in the grounds of Tynemouth Priory, near the church.

However, with reference to this particular legend, the pedestal of the cross was at one time said to have been engraved with the following inscription:

*"O horrid dede,
To kill a man for a pigges hede."*

The story is that one day, during the Middle Ages, a monk from Tynemouth Priory was out walking, and eventually arrived at Delaval Hall. Lord Delaval was out hunting but expected back for dinner, which was being lavishly prepared as the monk arrived. One dish, specifically ordered for the Lord himself, was a pig, a delicacy which the monk was unable to resist. He cut off the pig's head, regarded as the best part of the animal, and putting it in a bag, set off to return to the monastery.

When Lord Delaval returned to the Hall, he took the loss as a personal insult, and immediately remounted his horse, galloping furiously after the offender. Having caught up with the monk near

25

Preston, Delaval hit the holy man repeatedly and brutally, with his staff, so that the unfortunate man could hardly crawl back to the monastery.

The monk died later within a year and a day, and although the beating was not the entire cause of his death, his fellow brethren charged Lord Delaval with his murder. In order to absolve himself, Delaval was obliged to give valuable estates to the Priory, including the manor of Elswick in Newcastle, which became the summer residence for the Priors of Tynemouth. He was also made to do penance for his dreadful deed, and to set up a stone in the place where he had attacked the monk:

"Now at this day, while years roll on,
And the knight doth coldly lie,
The stone doth stand on the silent land,
To tellen the strangers nigh,
That a horrid dede for a pig his hede
Did thence to heavenward cry."

Many of the legends connected with stones are concerned with the possibility of finding treasure hidden beneath them. A huge ancient stone once stood in the field of a farm near Haltwhistle, and was haunted by a tragic ghost. The apparition took the form of a melancholy lady dressed in loose grey clothes, who became known as 'Nelly the Knocker', for she spent many nights sitting on the rock, feebly knocking on it with a small stone.

As the ghost was fairly quiet and harmless, the farmer and his family were not afraid and did not disturb it. 'Nelly' was left in peace for many years until a new farmer arrived and his two sons became curious about the strange knocking. They watched 'Nelly' closely, and soon began to imagine that the boulder concealed buried treasure.

Although their father was reluctant to disturb the ghost, he finally agreed to allow the two brothers to blast the stone with gunpowder from a local quarry. One afternoon when 'Nelly' was nowhere to be seen, the boys carried out their plan. There was a huge explosion as fragments of stone flew in all directions. Clearing away the debris, the brothers found a large hollow, closely packed with urns, each filled with gold coins. So great was the treasure,

26

that they were wealthy for the rest of their lives, but 'Nelly the Knocker' was never seen again.

In a field between Lilburn and Middleton, near Morpeth, there was said to be a stone of religious significance, which according to the superstition of the time, was not to be removed. Two local farm workers, however, were determined to solve the mystery surrounding the stone. One night, they went to the field, armed with spades and other necessary equipment, not telling anyone of their intentions.

Having dug for some time to a considerable depth, they began to think that the tales of buried treasure, guarded by demons, must be untrue. Suddenly, they felt a movement from the ground below. Terrified, but blinded by the thought of buried treasure and their greed, they continued digging. Again, the earth quaked and shuddered, and a creature, resembling a swan, flapped its wings and flew out of the pit, emitting a strange and hideous cry.

Horror- struck, the peasants threw down their spades and ran to escape the grasp of the evil creature. The sanctuary of the stone was left inviolate from that very day.

On the footpath leading to Harbottle Hill, about a mile from Harbottle in Coquetdale, stands the Drake Stone, a large block of reddish-grey grit, twenty seven feet in height. A story is told of how the local people were awoken one summer morning by cries of help.

A stranger, having arrived at the village the previous night and taken refreshment in the local inn, decided to climb the stone. Inspired perhaps by the 'refreshment', he accomplished the climb easily but was unable to face the yawning descent. Having spent a sleepless, miserable night on the cold rock, he was rescued by the local people next morning.

Finally , there is a legend connected to the Blue Stone, which lies near the Lion Tower at Warkworth Castle. Many centuries ago, the custodian of the castle, having dreamt three times in succession that treasure lay under a stone in the castle grounds, innocently told a neighbour about his dreams.

Two or three days passed before the custodian decided to investigate and found that a trench which he had not seen before, had recently been dug beside the blue stone. Soon after, his neighbour mysteriously became very rich!

OF WORMS, DRAGONS, SERPENTS AND THE LIKE
❖••❖••❖••❖••❖••❖••❖••❖

Combing through the various accounts of the legends concerning these strange creatures, references are found to *"worms, serpents, boars and dragons"*. Sir Walter Scott in his *'Minstrelsy of the Border'* explains their existence by suggesting that in the days before Britain was cleared of swamps and woods, these large beasts would have infested forests, causing death and terror among the local population. This opinion was also held by the eminent historian, Surtees, although he always referred to the creatures as "worms".

There are several legends concerning the worms interspersed throughout our local folklore, two of the most well-known being 'The Lambton Worm' and 'The Laidley Worm of Spindleston'. (*For a retelling of these stories see our book entitled: 'Ghosts and Legends of Northumbria'.*)

Two other tales, the 'Pollard Worm' and the 'Worm of Sockburn', are set in the county of Durham and contain marked similarities. The Pollard Worm is often depicted as an enormous boar. It roamed the land in and around Bishop Auckland, ravaging the countryside and terrifying the local population. Many gallant hunters and knights lost their lives trying to kill the beast. The situation became so desperate that the king offered a substantial sum of money to anyone who could bring him the boar's head at Westminster. The Bishop of Durham also pledged a reward.

Many tried and failed, but finally an expert hunter, a very brave young man named Pollard, succeeded in trapping and killing it. One day the brave knight, having tracked down the boar, tethered his horse and climbed a beech tree in the forest and shook down *"a large quantity of beechmast"*.

Shortly he had the satisfaction of seeing the beast arrive and *"feed voraciously on the beechmast."* Having eaten its fill, the boar showed signs of drowsiness and began to move away. Pollard decided to take action and began his attack. Despite the huge meal and its tiredness, the boar still put up a strong resistance and the battle lasted most of the night. As dawn broke the brave knight severed the beast's head and cut out its tongue to place in his wallet.

Exhausted, he fell into a deep sleep and awoke to find that the head had vanished. Bitterly disappointed, he realised he did not have the trophy to show the King and so he rode to tell the Bishop of his exploits and showed him the beast's tongue.

The Bishop of Durham was overjoyed, the boar was dead, and in his delight and relief Pollard was told he was entitled to all the land he could ride around whilst the Bishop dined. The acres involved became known thereafter as 'Pollard's Land'.

A ceremony was enacted which was repeated whenever the Bishop visited his castle. He would be met by a member of the Pollard family and presented with a sword. The original speech made with the gift of land and repeated at the ceremony was:

"My Lord, on behalf of myself, as well as others, possessors of the Pollard's lands, do humbly present your Lordship with this falchion, at your first coming here, wherewith, as the tradition goeth, he slew of old a venomous serpent, which did much harm to man and beast, and by performing this service we hold our lands."

The Bishop would graciously reply with thanks and wishes for the health and happiness of the Pollard family, and return the sword. The crest of the Pollard family became, and remained, an arm holding a broad curved sword.

A similar tale which involves the 'Worm of Sockburn' took place eight miles from Newsham, the most southern point of the County of Durham. One account dates the time of the deed as 1063 when one Sir John Conyers *"slew a venomous dragon who was devouring men, women and children."*

"And in this limpid stream we find the Lords
Of Sogburn meet the Bishop new elect;
To him they homage pay with great respect.

...They hold a sword, and tell a wond'rous tale
Of a wing'd serpent which did infest
Sogburn's fine plains, of Durham lands the best...

...a deliverer to the oppress'd
Arose, whose name was Conyers, he a wight,

29

Did, like Alcides, in great deeds delight:
In his own prowess wrapt, and coat of mail,
He with his sword this serpent did assail...'

The presentation ceremony which also involves the giving of a sword is supposed to date from the time of Bishop Pudsey, who purchased from Richard I the title of Earl of Sadberge. The Bishop of Durham would be met by the Lord of the Manor of Sockburn on Croft Bridge over the River Tees and, having exchanged greetings, the following declaration was made as the falchion was handed over:

"My Lord Bishop, I here present you with the falchion where with the champion Conyers slew the worm, dragon and fiery flying serpent which destroyed man, woman and child; in memory of which the king then reigning gave him the manor of Sockburn, to hold by this tenure, that upon the first entrance of every bishop into the county this falchion should be presented."

Mention of the land tenure appears in the inquest into the death of a later Sir John Conyers in 1396. The sword itself appears in the painted glass of a window in Sockburn Church, and together with the worm, is sculptured in marble on the tomb of an ancestor of the Conyers family. The falchion used to be kept at the manor house of Sockburn and was described as follows:

"The blade is broad, and two feet five inches long, and on the pommel of the weapon are two shields; on one side are the three lions of England, as borne by the Plantagenet monarchs from John to Edward III, and the eagle displayed on the other side is said to belong to Morcar, the Saxon Earl of Northumberland."

The last known enactment of the Sockburn ceremony was recorded as April 1826 when a steward of Sir Edward Blackett presented a sword to Dr.Van Mildert, the last Prince Bishop of Durham.

VAMPIRES OF THE BORDER
✠•✠•✠•✠•✠•✠•✠•✠•✠

It seems that vampires and the like were not just restricted to Eastern Europe, but were active here on our own doorstep, not only the famous 'Dracula' at Whitby, but also nearer home, at Berwick and Melrose for example.

The tale concerning the vampire at Berwick was first told by the highly respected Canon William of Newburgh, and took place during the reign of Richard I in the thirteenth century. The plague was continually sweeping the country at this time, wiping out whole towns and villages - Berwick being no exception to this devastating pestilence.

A rich merchant, thought to have been a victim of the plague, had been regarded, in life, as a religious man continually carrying out good deeds. However, after his death, his fellow citizens discovered that he had, in fact, led a corrupt, criminal life and he was refused a burial in consecrated ground. Shortly after his funeral, strange and terrible events took place in the town.

The man, having lived a sinful life, was not allowed to rest in his grave, and each night he rose from his tomb in search of human flesh and blood amongst the townsfolk. As he rushed, demented, through the streets, a pack of howling dogs pursued him night after night, their wild baying allowing the citizens no rest. The hounds pursued the vampire back to his tomb as daylight apporached only to renew the hunt as darkness fell.

The tormented spirit was heard to shout,

"Until my body is burnt, you folk of Berwick shall have no peace!"

The people of the town dare not venture out at night as the

"deadly monster ...with a ravenous appetite for human flesh, bent on manner of mischief to the living, biting every person that came in his way and either worrying them to death or driving them stark mad."

Finally it was decided that these events could not be allowed to

31

continue and a meeting was held to decide how to end the vampire's nightly reign of terror. Ten brave young men were either hired or volunteered to exhume the merchant's corpse, dismember the body and burn it until only ashes remained.

The inhabitants had hoped to avert any further tragedies in the town, but shortly after the destruction of the vampire, plague again swept through Berwick, decimating the population. It is said that as the plague victims were carried to their graves, some people still claimed to hear the distant baying of the hounds and the fearful screams of the vampire.

A similar incident which took place at Melrose was also told by William of Newburgh. The vampire in this case, had been a 'worldly' priest, enjoying the material pleasures of life, but his great love was hunting and he became known as the 'Hundeprest' or 'Dog-Priest'.

After his death, his former mistress complained that he was haunting her bedchamber, terrifying her with his loud moans and groans. She appealed to the church for help and two monks and two young lay-men, well armed, kept watch over the grave of the former priest. They paced restlessly at the graveside, as the fallen leaves crackled beneath their feet and a grey mist swirled up around them from the River Tweed.

Expecting the Hundeprest to show himself at midnight, the hour passed without incident, and being chilled to the bone, three of them sought shelter and warmth in a nearby cottage. No sooner had they left, than the Hundeprest, now a terrible monster, rushed at the remaining priest. The monk bravely stood his ground and swung his axe, driving it deep into the vampire. Groaning, the monster fled, the monk in pursuit, until it disappeared back into its own grave.

The other three watchers returned but saw nothing, and at the first light of dawn the four men began to open up the grave. As they dug, blood oozed up through the clay and when the corpse was finally revealed, it was found to be as fresh as when it was originally buried, apart from a gaping wound, bleeding profusely. They bore the terrible remains away from the monastery, the dead monk not fit to be within its sight, and burned the corpse to ashes, the wind sweeping away all final traces.

THE HAND THAT DID NOT PERISH
❖••❖••❖••❖••❖••❖••❖••❖

After Edwin, the first Christian King of Northumbria, was killed in battle, his kingdom was again divided into its original provinces of Bernicia and Deira. Eanfrid, the son of Edwin's predecessor, became ruler of Bernicia, and Osric, Edwin's cousin, King of Deira. Their triumph however, was shortlived, as the barbarous Cadwalla, King of Strathclyde, slew them both in battle, and became ruler in their stead.

Eanfrid's younger brother, Oswald, was determined to rescue his country from the terrible cruelty and tyranny of Cadwalla. Gathering a small army, he marched to meet Cadwalla at Heavenfield, near the Roman Wall. Here Oswald erected a simple wooden cross, and on his knees prayed to God to help him and his followers defeat their enemy.

Cadwalla was slain in the fierce battle that took place, and his army was scattered. It was claimed as a tremendous victory of 'right over might' and became known as the first decisive triumph of Christianity over Paganism in this country. Many miracles are said to have happened at this spot, which today is marked by a roughcast cross.

Now that his enemies were disposed of, Oswald set about restoring the Christian faith to his kingdom. Sending to friends in Scotland, where he had been taught during his exile, he arranged for a priest to come and teach his people.

At first the experiment was not successful. The people would not listen to Corman, the first monk to be sent, and he was forced to return to Iona and admit defeat. In his place, however, came Aidan, who quickly won the hearts of all he met. King Oswald made him Bishop of Lindisfarne and himself acted as an interpreter between Aidan and the people. Together they founded many churches, two of the most famous being Bamburgh and Lindisfarne.

King Oswald himself ruled wisely and well, and was much loved for his unfailing generosity to the poor and needy. He became known as 'Oswald of the Fair Hand' following the events one Easter day when he was dining with Aidan at Bamburgh. As they were about to say grace, servants told them that there were several poor people outside begging for food. The King immediately sent out not only his own dinner, but the huge silver dish on which it had been served. This was broken up and distributed among the people. So impressed was Bishop Aidan by this act, that seizing the King's right hand, he declared : *"May this hand never perish."*

Just a few years later however, in 642, the good King Oswald was killed in battle by Penda of Mercia. The place where it happened is believed by some sources to have been Oswestry - 'Oswalds' Tree'- in Shropshire. The body of the king was taken to Bardsley in Lincolnshire to be buried. Whilst it lay overnight in a tent, a marvellous light was seen to glow around the whole area, and miracles were reported later to have happened there.

Legend relates variously that Oswald's right hand and arm were cut off during the terrible slaughter, or that the body was mutilated by his enemies after death. In either event his faithful followers managed to gain possesion of them. Transported to Bamburgh, the relics were placed in a silver casket in St. Peter's Chapel, where they became a focus of pilgrimage throughout the Middle Ages.

It is said that, many years after Oswald's death, Bede witnessed the opening of the casket when the hand and arm were found to be intact. Thus was fulfilled the prophesy of Aidan : *"the hand that did not perish"*.

THE MAGIC OINTMENT
✥•✥•✥•✥•✥•✥•✥•✥•✥

There are many tales and legends associated with fairies, usually relating how human beings suffered as a result of having tricks played on them by the fairy folk. From time to time fairies had to call on humans for help, but if they did not do exactly as the fairies asked, they were dealt severe punishments.

The first such incident concerns a midwife, known locally as the 'Howdie', who lived near Elsdon in Northumberland. One particular night she was awoken by a messenger on horseback who begged her assistance and asked her to accompany him to a secret place. She would be blindfolded for the journey, but would receive an ample reward for her services. Hesitating only for a moment, she accompanied the strange rider, travelling only a short distance, before she was shown into a small cottage. Her blindfold now removed, she found herself in a warm and comfortable room, but she did not recognise it, or the beautiful lady who required her help.

Once the baby was delivered, an old woman, who appeared to be the lady's nurse, gave the 'Howdie' a box of ointment and asked her to anoint the baby's eyes. However, under no circumstances should it touch her own eyes. Afraid to disobey any of these instructions, the midwife did as she was told, but feeling an irritation in her eye, subconsciously rubbed at it. Instantly, the scene before her changed. She found herself in a wood; a hollow tree stood where the fireplace had been, the sofa was a bed of moss and the lamps were glow worms. Realising that her patients were fairies, the Howdie remained calm and did not reveal the secrets which had unfolded before her. Having completed her task, she was escorted home by the messenger, her pockets heavy with fairy gold.

A few days later, shopping at the local market, she saw the old fairy woman going from stall to stall scraping a little butter from each display, carefully storing it in a container at her side. As they came face to face it was obvious to the old crone that the 'Howdie' had recognised her, so she asked: *"Which eye do you see me with?"* The midwife answered innocently: *"With the left eye"*. Blowing into her face, the fairy cried,*"Well then, take that!"* The midwife was

35

immediately blinded in her left eye for the rest of her life.

A similar trick was played on a country doctor. He, too, was called out urgently by a mysterious messenger who led him some distance into the hills. Eventually they stopped at an isolated place and the guide instructed the doctor to rub his eyes with ointment from a small box. As he did so he saw a splendid entrance built into the side of the hill, and on entering, found himself in a magnificent, richly decorated fairy hall. Having attended to the patient inside, as he came out the guide again instructed the doctor to rub his eyes with the ointment. He put the salve on one eye, but pretended to rub the other in order that he could enter the fairy world again whenever he wished. A few days later at Morpeth market, he recognised the fairy stealing corn. As he challenged him, the fairy blew into his face and from that time the doctor was totally blind.

A third tale relates how a fairy couple took their child to a cottager and his wife at Netherwitton, near Morpeth. The three arrived at the cottage late one night, and although dressed in ordinary clothes, had an air of royalty about them. They explained to the childless couple that they had to travel away for some time and asked if they might leave the boy, paying generously for his keep.

The cottager and his wife were so pleased to be having the child, they refused the money and promised to take great care of him. The father then produced a jar of ointment and asked the couple to anoint the child's eyes every night, but under no circumstances should they use it themselves.

The cottager spent many a sleepless night thinking about the ointment, and on many occasions almost succumbed and used it on himself. Eventually, he did give way to temptation and applied it to one eye, with no immediate results. Thinking it was a special cream to improve the child's sight, he contented himself and thought no more about it.

Later, spending a day at Longhorsley Fair, he saw the child's father, the king of the fairies in fact, stealing butter and cheeses, invisible to everyone but the old man. Approaching the fairy, he accused him of thieving, and the fairy asked which eye he could see him with. Unthinking, the cottager pointed to the anointed eye. The fairy blew on the eye and the sight was lost. The man ran to tell his wife, but the child had disappeared, together with his fairy parents.

THE SIMONSIDE DWARFS

✢✣✢✣✢✣✢✣✢✣✢✣✢

The Simonside Hills and the surrounding moorland near Rothbury were said to be the haunt of mischievous dwarfs. These were small, ugly creatures who waylaid travellers, leading them into marshy ground and causing them to lose their way on the lonely tracks. They were always out after dark and shepherds keeping a lonely vigil in the hills claimed to have seen them often.

One man decided to dispel these myths and prepared to spend a night in the hills in order to show that such beings did not exist. Wrapped in warm clothing, his staff in his hand, he wandered around for some time seeing nothing. As he was about to return home, he decided to pretend that he was lost and in the local dialect shouted, *"Tint! Tint!"*

Immediately a light shone ahead of him, such as could be seen in the window of a shepherd's cottage, and he stepped cautiously towards it. He soon found himself in marshy ground, and realising what was happening, picked up a loose piece of turf and threw it into the bog, pretending that he had fallen to his fate. The light was instantly extinguished and thinking that he had fooled the little creatures, he turned back once more and shouted : *"Tint! Tint!"*

At this the dwarfs *"with hideous visages"* showed themselves and ran after him with lighted torches. Trying to escape, the shepherd saw that he was completely surrounded by the ugly dwarfs, each carrying a lighted torch and a club. As they advanced towards him, waving their clubs, he struck out at them with his staff, appearing to knock one over, although *"his offensive weapon encountered in its descent no substance of flesh or bone."* In fact, the dwarves appeared to multiply before his very eyes, their evil faces twisted with menace, their clubs held aloft.

The absolute horror of the situation completely overwhelmed him, and he fell unconscious to the ground, where he lay until dawn. By then the imps had retreated and he was able to return safely home.

Another such incident concerns a traveller walking towards Rothbury who had strayed from the right path and lost his way, and

37

was looking for shelter. Seeing a light in the distance, he made his way up a steep path towards it, and found an old wooden hut probably used by shepherds during the lambing season. As he entered, he saw a wood fire burning between two rough grey stones that could be used for seats. There were two wooden gate posts near the fire to be used as fuel, as well as some kindling lying on the ground. Relieved at his good fortune, the man built up the fire and sat down on one of the stones.

After a short time, a small figure, no higher than his knee, walked into the hut and, without saying a word, sat down on the remaining stone. Having been warned about dwarfs in the hills, the traveller did not move or speak, but, as the fire blazed he stared at the dwarf.

Later the fire began to die down and the air turned cold. The man began to shiver, but the dwarf appeared unaffected by the chill. As the traveller reached to break some of the smaller sticks to rekindle the fire, the creature gave the man a look of total contempt, and picked up one of the old gate posts, breaking it effortlessly over his knee, and threw the pieces into the fire.

The man did not move again, thinking that if he tried to imitate the dwarf with the other post, he would be falling into a trap set by the mischievous devil. They sat on motionless in the darkness and when dawn broke, the man found himself alone.

Not only had the dwarf vanished, but the hut was no longer there, only the ashes of the fire remained. Most terrifying of all, however, the stone on which he sat was situated at the edge of a precipice - how thankful he was that he had remained still throughout his ordeal!

THE BROWN MAN OF THE MOORS

❖❖❖❖❖❖❖❖❖

When the Archangel Michael removed the evil spirits from heaven they appeared on earth, assuming the form of dwarfs or brownies, taking delight in playing tricks on unsuspecting humans. One legend related to this tradition concerns the 'Brown Man of the Moors' and a Border chieftan known as the 'Cowt of Kielder', because of his physical strength and skill.

His sworn enemy was Lord Soulis, then owner of Hermitage Castle, positioned on the opposite side of the Border to Kielder Castle. The land to the south west of their respective castles caused many skirmishes between them as they argued over its ownership. Lord Soulis, an ugly and treacherous man, was constantly harrassing his neighbours and believed all of life's events were governed by good and evil spirits.

In view of this, the Lord of Kielder was naturally astounded to receive an invitation to dine with Lord Soulis at Hermitage Castle. Sensing danger, the Cowt's wife begged him not to go and called on the Brown Man of the Moors, who appeared, prophesying danger. The Cowt, however, was undaunted and wore charmed armour which could not be pierced, placing sprays of holly and rowan leaves in his helmet to ward off evil spirits.

"In Keeldar's plume the holly green,
And rowan leaves, nod on."

Unfortunately, events quickly revealed that his secret charms to keep the spirits at bay had been betrayed to Lord Soulis by the Brown Man. After dinner at Hermitage Castle, the Cowt's men were unable to move - a spell had been cast upon them. Only the Cowt, due to his magic armour, was able to rise from the table.

As he made his escape, Lord Soulis' men pursuing him, he slipped while crossing a burn and fell into the water. The magic of the armour and rowan leaves was useless in running water and the Lord's men held the Cowt under the water until he drowned, his rowan and holly leaves floating away down stream.

39

"And now young Keeldar reach'd the stream,
Above the foamy linn;
The Border lances round him gleam,
And force the warrior in.

The holly floated to the side,
And the leaf of the rowan pale;
Alas! no spell could charm the tide;
Nor the lance of Liddlesdale."

The Cowt was buried in a gigantic grave on the banks of the North Tyne with two ancient grey stones at his head and feet. Lord Soulis met his end plotting against Robert the Bruce and the Cowt's men remained spellbound at Hermitage Castle.

The Brown Man of the Moors continued to haunt the area and another tale concerning him took place in the eighteenth century. In 1714 two young men journeyed from Newcastle to Elsdon for a day's shooting on the moors. Tired after their exertions, they sat down by a stream to drink from the clear water. Having quenched their thirst they looked up to see a man, stout and broad but half the height of a normal human being. He was dressed entirely in brown, with wild red hair above a ferocious savage face, and staring eyes.

Addressing the younger of the two men, the dwarf demanded angrily, *"Do you know who I am?"* The young man, unsure of himself, replied that if the dwarf was the Lord of the Manor, they would be pleased to return the game they had killed. The dwarf's anger subsided slightly, and he refused the meat saying he ate only wild fruits and berries, with a few mushrooms when they were available, regarding himself as the protector of birds and animals.

He suggested that the men join him for a meal as he had a plentiful supply of fruits in the wood. The younger man turned to tell his companion of the invitation, but when he turned back to accept, the tiny man had disappeared.

The two youths, having enjoyed their day's sport returned home to Newcastle. However, soon the youth who had spoken to the dwarf, became very ill with a cold and died shortly afterwards. People maintained that it was the vengeance of the Brown Man of the Moors.

40

THE WIZARD'S CAVE

Tales of buried treasure guarded by fearsome dragons waiting for a brave knight to break the spells - these are as numerous and as popular today as hundreds of years ago. Several folktales relate similar stories with good luck or ill to the person who stumbles across the treasure.

Here is such a story, set in the coastal town of Tynemouth. On the north side of the Priory there used to be a very famous cave, known variously as 'Jingling Geordies' Hole', 'Jingling Man's Hole' or the 'Wizard's Cave'. Mothers would excite the imagination of their children by telling them the legend:

"by Tinmouth's towers grey,
Where chant the cowl'd monks by night and day,
In a cavern of rock scoop'd under the sea
Lye treasures in keeping of Sorcerie.
It avails not the cross were sainted and true,
It avails not the prayers of the Prior Sir Hugh,
It avails not, O Dread, Holy Virgin's fond care,
Great treasure long held by dark Satan is there."

The description told of a cave entered through an arched doorway which contained two chambers, in one of which was a hole about twelve feet deep leading to two small vaults. Here, as the legend tells, there was a treasure house of gold, jewels and precious stones guarded by frightful dragons and demons. It would need a very brave person to break the spells and reach the treasure.

Walter the Bold was a famous and courageous knight who had fought valiantly in many battles. He had heard the story of the treasure, perhaps at his mother's knee, and was determined to claim it for himself. Having travelled to Tynemouth, he set out one dark night armed with a sword and a lamp to reach the cave. Scrambling over the rocks he reached the entrance and pushed his way into a narrow tunnel.

Immediately he was attacked from all sides by fearsome

41

dragons, hob-goblins, hell-dogs and all manner of terrifying demons. Bravely he struck out with his sword refusing to be turned back. The demons pursued him to the edge of a yawning gap and shrieked with maniacal glee at his dismay when he saw the width and depth of the hole.

Summoning all his courage, Walter removed the heavier parts of his armour, said a quick prayer, took a deep breath and leapt across the gap. Safely on the other side, the demons left helpless behind, he approached a massive door. Beside the door on a golden chain, hung a bugle which Walter seized and on which he blew three long and loud blasts. A magic cock crew, and the door burst open.

In amazement and wonder Walter gazed into a huge chamber lined with twelve crystal pillars on which hung twelve golden lamps. Their light was reflected across the chamber floor which was piled high with gold, silver, diamonds, emeralds, rubies and flashing beryls; twelve golden lamps shed a soft and serene light from the magic dome; while on twelve altars of onyx-stone incense burned.

"it may not be sung what treasures were seen,
Gold heaped upon gold, and emeralds green,
And diamonds, and rubies and sapphires untold
Rewarded the courage of Walter the Bold"

The story does not relate how Walter found his way back out of the cave, whether the demons were lying in wait for him, and how he managed to remove the treasure from its hiding place. It is told, however, that he became a rich lord of a hundred castles with vast estates, founded a monastery, married a beautiful princess, and lived a long and happy life. A very satisfying end to his adventures.

Legend also claims that the caves were thereafter haunted by sounds of dragging chains and moans - enough to scare anyone from trying to follow in Walter's footsteps. In spite of the rumours of hauntings, various accounts of further explorations of the caves are recorded. By the 1880's however, a landslip had destroyed the cave entrance, leaving only two unremarkable small caves accessible.

There are said still to be undiscovered vaults and passages beneath Tynemouth Castle, so perhaps some of the treasure trove remains there to this day.

THE WISE MAN OF STOKESLEY
❖❖❖❖❖❖❖❖❖

Mr. Wrightson, widely acknowledged in South Durham and Cleveland as the 'The Wise Man of Stokesley', flourished around 1800. He achieved such prominence in the local neighbourhood that his presence was immediately called for, by all classes of society, on the occasion of any sickness, concern about property or other matters.

Although his private personality was said to be *"very bad"* he was constantly asked to be godfather to the local children and on these occasions he would attend church *"in a scarlet coat, a long white waistcoat and full-starched shirt frill, crimson knee-breeches, and white stockings."*

Wrightson always claimed that he had no special knowledge or powers above other men, except when he was fasting and then he owed his powers to being the seventh son of a seventh daughter, but was unable to transmit them to his own son. Several stories were related and passed on by eye witnesses at the time.

One such tale was told by a man at Danby whose relative had a cow which fell ill of a disease which *"baffled every cow-leech in the neighbourhood."* The man was mounted on a horse and despatched post haste to Stokesley to consult the wise man. After opening his door, not allowing the man to speak, the wizard said *"I know what has brought you here; you have come about a cow, and if I cannot tell you as much about the creature as you can tell me, it is not likely I can help you."*

He went on to describe the cow's colour, appearance and her symptoms which were a constant restlessness and strange movements together with an odd sound which she made. The wise man also knew her exact position in the byre - *"The door opened, right upon her rump..."* He specified the disease but claimed nothing could save her and she later died, the post-mortem confirming all that Wrightson had said.

Another incident involved pitmen working at the Try-Up Trough Pits. One day they left their clothes above, as usual, and went down into the pit. However, later in the day, the work

43

finished, one of the men could not find his shirt and, borrowing one from a friend, set off to consult the wise man accompanied by his friend Elijah. On the way they passed a place called West House where Elijah left his overcoat saying to his friend that they could test the reliability of the old man's answers about the shirt by asking him if he knew where the coat was.

Again, as the wise man answered their knock he immediately related the reason for their visit before they had the chance to speak. He then turned to Elijah and asked *"What hast 'ee deean wi thy coat Elijah? I think thee'st lossit a' West House. Think'st 'ee t' wise man knaws aught about t'shart?"*

As these words were exactly those which Elijah had used, he was dumbfounded. The wizard described the shirt saying, correctly, that it had been made by a left handed person and that the owner would find it at home. He added a final warning about the dangers of giving away salt from the house, an act which the pitman's mother was guilty of that day. On returning home they found the shirt and discovered that the lady of the house had, in fact, given away salt that day.

The next story is about a miller who mysteriously lost a set of weights and, his search having been in vain, consulted the wise man. Having looked at his books, the wizard declared that the weights would be restored and were at present hidden in an *"ass-midden"*. After a couple of nights they re-appeared *"all clammed wi' ass."*

On another occasion a young bull became ill and despite all remedies was soon dying, too weak to stand, and was supported by ropes to prevent it from falling. The wise man was sent for and as usual said that unless he could tell them all they could tell him and a little more, it was unlikely that he could be of use. Eventually he lit his pipe and agreed to look at the beast. After a while, two of the men followed him to the byre and were amazed to see the bull looking well, standing unaided and heartily eating his food. Alas, the cure remained a secret.

After the old man's death, William Dawson, who rented a farm in the area, inherited some of the wise man's books and continued his trade. He too gained recognition for his skills but his powers did not gain him fame and fortune, or even enable him to continue his present life style. He sank into poverty and died in South Durham in poor circumstances.

One story is related of his style of treatment. A wealthy farmer had sustained heavy losses from his stock and asked Dawson to find out if witchcraft was the cause of the disaster. The farmer was told to take six knots of 'bottree'(bore-tree or elder) wood and after placing them in an orderly fashion under a new ashen bowl or platter, was to leave them. If, when he looked at them again some time later they were scattered untidily, witchcraft was definitely at work.

The farmer carried out these instructions and the knots of wood were found to be in *"utter confusion"*. He was then told to remove the heart from one of the dead beasts and pierce it with nine new nails, nine new pins, and the same number of new needles. Having done this, the heart was to be burnt on a fire made and fed from witch-wood (rowan tree) and just before midnight a certain verse of the Bible was to be recited over the flames and then the spell would be broken.

On the appointed night the farmhouse was locked and bolted as the heart lay on the fire and at midnight, as the farmer touched it with the poker it *"burst asunder"* into pieces. Gathering them together on the hot embers, he read the verse and *"at the same moment a rushing and clattering was heard down the paved causey which led from the house to the turnpike in front, as if a carrriage and pair came driven down it furiously."* There was then a terrible knocking and hammering at first the front door and then the back, but as the last spark of the fire disappeared so the noise ceased and the farmer's herd was no longer in danger.

A final story is told of how Dawson restored the health of a young man thought to be bewitched. Again, a fire was made as before and all doors and windows were closed.

"Clippings from every finger and toe nail of the patient, with hair from each temple, and the crown of his head, were stuffed into the throat of a pigeon which had previously been placed between the patient's feet, and there had died at once, thus attesting the witchery from which he was suffering. The bird's bill was rivetted with three pins, and then the wise man thrust a pin into its breast, to reach the heart, everybody else in the room in turn following his example. An opening was then made in the fire, and the pigeon dropped into it. The wise man began to read aloud Psalms

45

from the Prayer Book, and a loud scratching and whining began outside."

Everyone in the house agreed that the evil spirit had gone from the young man and had now appeared outside, possibly in the form of a dog. Only the young man sceptically attributed the noise to the wise man's own dog but he annoyed Dawson and his friends so much by voicing this opinion, he would have been wise to keep quiet.

❖❖❖❖❖

Black Jock of Newcastle was another wizard or wise man who was often consulted by local people. In one instance a local farmer whose horse had died in suspicious circumstances, suspected a spiteful neighbour of foul play. He took the problem to Black Jock who declared that the horse had been killed by poison, given to it in brewers grain.

On the payment of a pound, he gave the farmer the following instructions to uncover the poisoner. He and a friend were to secretly dissect the horse and remove its heart. They should then stick pins in the heart and roast it over a fire between eleven and twelve o'clock at night, having first ensured that the room was airtight. As the clock struck midnight they should open the door and would see the guilty person passing by.

The wizard's instruction were carried out to the letter but as they opened the door at the appointed time it happened that one of their most respectable and trustworthy neighbours was passing. They could hardly accuse such a man and reported back to the wizard.

After examining the house, Black Jock discovered a certain round hole in the stairs where air had been able to get through. He insisted that there was no appeal against their carelessness and that they would now never see the guilty party.

Another farmer suffered a similar incident with his horse and carried out Black Jock's instructions. However, the watchers' claimed to have heard spirits howling around the house and satisfied themselves that these were the evil spirits which had killed their horse.

CHARMS, CURES AND SUPERSTITIONS

A stone with a hole in it suspended at the head of a bed prevents nightmares.

The cure for a sprained arm was a brown paper bandage with a charm on it.

Those who were short sighted *"ate little meat, combed their heads and drank wormword."* On Tweedside a talisman known as a lammerbead (lammer being the Scottish word for amber) would act as a cure in the hands of a particular witch woman. The stone, dug out of a British grave or barrow, was passed over the inflamed eyes.

Toothache was believed to have been originally caused by eating forbidden fruit. Even after a tooth had been removed it was believed that there was still a connection between it and the gums. If the tooth was thrown away and allowed to rot you would suffer an infection until the tooth finally dissolved away. To prevent this, salt was placed in the hollow part of the removed tooth and it was then thrown into the fire.

Toothache was also believed to be caused by worms, the remedy was this:

"take an old holly leaf and one of the lower umbels of hartwort, and the upward part of sage, boil two doles (this is, two of worts to one of water) in water, pour into a bowl, and yawn over it, and the worms will fall into the bowl."

Laying a trout on the stomach was said to cure worms, and drinking the water in which earth worms had been boiled was also thought to bring relief.

If you suffered a pain in the side a sharn (skin) of an old swine was warmed and laid on thickly. A thigh ache was cured by smoking the thigh thoroughly with fern.

To cure a snake bite wax should be removed from the ears and the wound anointed while repeating the prayer of St. John.

Anyone who lost their voice should swallow butter mingled with wheaten meal nine mornings running.

A poison victim should be made to stand on their head while their legs were whipped and the poison would then run out of the incisions.

47

Earache was cured with a salve of hen's fat and the shells of oysters.
Anyone showing signs of madness was to be whipped with a whip made from the skin of a porpoise.
Cows whose milk dried up were said to be bewitched. The cure for this was to place a pair of breeches on the animal's head and to beat her around the field with a good thick cudgel.
The docken was a charm connected with the medicinal application of the dock leaf. Anyone stung by a nettle should spit on the leaves and rub the affected part repeating *"In docken, out docken"* until the stinging stops. This was an old saying used even in Chaucer's time in his 'Troilus and Cresseide'.
A cure for a sty on the eyelid was to touch it nine times with a wedding ring.
To cure epilectic fits one should beg a half crown, recently given at Holy Communion, from the priest and make it into a ring to be worn by the afflicted.
There were several charms and cures against warts. One was to wash the hands in water in which eggs had been boiled or to wash them nine times in water left after potatoes had been boiled. You could also rub a large black snail over the wart and then throw the poor creature against a thorn hedge. As the snail melted away from being impaled on a twig, so did the wart. The warts could also be rubbed with eel's blood or a piece of beef which should then be thrown away to rot - as it rots so should the warts disappear. An apple was cut in half and the warts rubbed with both halves which were then buried in the ground. As the apple decayed, the warts vanished.
An eel skin tied around the left leg was said to be a cure for cramp. A handful of sulphur or common brimstone could also be taken to bed and held all night. A sufferer could also wear a cramp ring made from the handle of a decayed coffin which was blessed by a priest on Good Friday. This was worn on the finger or placed on the limb affected by cramp.
To cure whooping cough, a trout's head was placed in the mouth of the sufferer, allowing the fish to breathe into the child's mouth. Other cures included making porridge over a stream which ran from north to south; tying a hairy caterpillar in a bag around the child's neck and as the insect died, the cough ceased; carrying a patient through a lime kiln; passing the sufferer under the belly of an ass or a piedbald pony. In Sunderland the crown of the head was shaved and the hair hung on a bush in the belief that the birds would take it to line their nests, together with the cough.

When a Northumbrian reaper cut his hand on a sickle, the tool was cleaned and polished. Similarly, if an injury was caused by a rusty nail, it was taken to the blacksmith's for the rust to be removed and was then rubbed carefully every day before sunrise and after sunset until the wound healed.

In the Borders the 'Black Penny' was a charm used to cure cattle afflicted with madness. The Penny was dipped in a well of water which ran towards the south and when enough water was drawn it was given to the sick animals. The lighting of 'need fires' took place when epidemics were present among the cattle. The fire was produced by rubbing two pieces of dry wood together and was carried from place to place as a charm against the cattle becoming infected. Bonfires were lit from the flame and the beasts were driven into the smoke and kept there for some time.

Irish stones, known to be favourite charms, were used in the Northumbrian Dales to prevent frogs, snails and other vermin entering the house. The Blessing bestowed by St. Patrick on the Emerald Isle was said to dwell in the stones and one charm belonging to a Thomas Hedley of Redesdale was described as a pale blue colour, three quarters of an inch in diameter and the same in thickness.

Lucky omens

It was considered lucky:
to carry a crooked sixpence or one with a hole in it.
to put a stocking on inadvertently inside out.
people with meeting eyebrows were thought to be fortunate.
to set a hen on an odd number of eggs (if she was set on an even number she would have no chickens).

Unlucky omens

It was considered unlucky:
for a hare to cross your path, or come running towards you as it was believed that witches could conceal their identity by taking the form of hares. A hare's foot was often nailed to the door and used as a charm against witches.

49

if you were standing on hard ground when hearing the first call of the cuckoo it would be a season of hardship. However, if you were standing on soft ground it would be an easy year.

a horse shoe charm was used to ward off evil and a round horse shoe representing the full moon was thought to be most effective.

to spill salt, but this could be avoided by throwing a pinch over the left shoulder. It was also considered unlucky to lend salt.

to throw tea leaves away - they should be placed on the back of the fire to keep poverty away.

General superstitions & beliefs

If two people wash together in the same basin, they will be sure to fall out before bedtime.

If your hair burns brightly when thrown in the fire, it is a sign of longevity but if it smoulders away, it is a sign of approaching death.

An itching nose is a sign of being cross, vexed or kissed by a fool. An itchy foot means you will tread on strange ground. An itching of the right hand means that you will receive money, while itching of the left means paying out money and an itchy ear portends sudden news.

You are being well-spoken of if your right ear tingles but someone is speaking ill of you if it is the left ear.

A sudden shiver means that someone is walking over your grave.

If you stumble going upstairs you will soon be married.

If you sing before breakfast you will cry before supper.

Putting a button into the wrong hole when dressing means that a misfortune will befall you that day.

A mole on the back of the neck means there is a danger of hanging.

If you eat pancakes on Shrove Tuesday and grey peas on Ash Wednesday, you will have money in your pockets all year.

If you have money in your pocket when you see a new moon you will not want for money all that month. However, it is unlucky to see the new moon first through the window or glass.

Spring can be said to have arrived when you can set your foot onto twelve daisies.

50

CUSTOMS OF BIRTH, MARRIAGE AND DEATH
✠✠✠✠✠✠✠✠

'MONDAY'S CHILD IS FAIR OF FACE'
Birth Customs

" *Monday's child is fair of face,*
Tuesday's child is full of grace,
Wednesday's child is full of woe,
And Thursday's child has far to go.
Friday's child is loving and giving
And Saturday's child works hard for its living;
But the child that is born on the Sabbath day,
Is blithe and bonny, good and gay."

When a birth was imminent the mother-to-be ensured that all bedding was cleaned and aired, and collected together clothing for the baby - similar to a modern mum arranging her layette. However, as death in childbirth was quite common, the prudent woman also laid aside a shift, a cap, a black ribbon and a pair of stockings in the event of a tragedy.

After the birth, which was attended by the midwife and often two or three female neighbours, and it was known that mother and baby were well, the celebrations could begin. As female friends, dressed in their Sunday best, arrived to see the child the evening became a lively one. A 'groaning cheese', loaf of bread, a few bottles of wine and one of spirits, usually whisky, were provided. The father of the new born infant had to cut a 'whang o' luck' from the cheese for the single ladies present, taking care not to cut his finger in case the child should die before reaching adulthood. The girls would then put the cheese under the pillows and hopefully dream of their lovers. In some parts of the north, people believed that in order for this to work, the cheese should first be pierced with pins from the infant's pin cushion.

The mother herself could not enter any of her friends' homes until she had attended a service at the chapel or church. Accompanied by her husband, either he or she took a portion of the

51

bread and cheese to give to the first person they met on the road as it was believed to be unlucky to go out empty handed. A slightly different variation was that the woman took the cheese and a bottle of whisky and the first person she gave it to, who was then thought to be lucky, had the privilege of giving money, if they had any, in exchange for the gift.

If the child was born in the top storey of a house and there were no stairs to the roof, someone holding the baby had to climb onto a stool or table in order to ensure that he or she would 'go up in the world.'

The first time the new baby was taken to a neighbour's house he or she was presented with a little salt - for luck, an egg - a symbol from ancient times signifying the source of life, and a piece of bread - to provide 'bodily sustenance'. These items, known as an 'Ammiss' bundle in South East Northumberland, were pinned into the child's shift. Other variations included giving the child a candle to light its way through life and a sixpence or other silver coin. This custom of giving a new-born child money is still carried on today, and it is common for neighbours to call, usually bringing a gift of new clothes or similar present for the baby.

A baby born with a caul, or membrane, over its head was thought to be lucky and would never die of drowning. Sailors would also preserve and take the cauls to sea to guard against drowning.

Baptism

In the Borders it was thought to be unlucky to tread on the graves of unbaptised children - 'unchristened ground'. Those who did unwittingly step on them ran the risk of getting a fatal disease known as 'grave-merels' or 'grave-scab'. This produced *"trembling of the limbs and hard breathing, and at last the skin burns as if touched with hot iron."* The remedy was to wear a sack, made as follows:

52

"The lint must be grown in a field which shall be manured from a farmyard keep that has not been disturbed for forty years. It must be spun by Old Habbitrot, that queen of spinsters. It must be bleached by an honest bleacher, in a honest miller's milldam and sewed by an honest tailor." Not an easy object to come by!

Some people thought it was lucky if a child cried at its baptism, if not, it was too good to live. Others felt that the cry was the voice of the evil spirit being driven out by the water. The baptism was thought to affect the child physically as well as spiritually, *"children never thrive until they have been christened."* The newly christened child was also made to sleep its first night in the cap it wore at the baptism.

In Durham if there was a boy and girl to be christened at the same time, the boy had to baptised first or it was believed that he would never achieve manhood and grow a beard. If the girl was christened first, it would be she who grew the beard!

'Better a child had ne'er been born
Than cut his nails on a Sunday morn!'

If a baby's nails were cut during its first year he or she would grow up to be a thief. The mother must bite them off if necessary, and in South East Northumberland it was believed that if the first nails were buried under an ash tree the child would be a good singer. In any event the nails should never be cut on a Sunday or a Friday.

❖❖❖❖❖❖

'SOMETHING OLD, SOMETHING NEW'
Marriage Customs

Each day of the week has its own particular virtue, or otherwise, as a day on which to be married:

"Monday for wealth,
Tuesday for health,
Wednesday the best day of all,

53

Thursday for losses,
Friday for crosses,
And Saturday no luck at all."

Omens

It was thought to be very unlucky for a swine to cross the path in front of the wedding party. A wedding after sunset forbode the bride would have a 'joyless' life, suffer the death of her children or go to an early grave herself. A wet day was thought to be very unlucky, while: *"Happy is the bride that the sun shines on."*

It was also unlucky for a woman to marry a man whose surname began with the same letter as her own:

> *"If you change the name and not the letter,*
> *You change for worse and not for better."*

To attend church on the day the banns were read out would result in a future child being born deaf or dumb. A wife who lost her wedding ring would lose her husband's affections and if the ring broke, death was imminent.

"Something old, something new, Something borrowed, something blue."

This custom, still carried out today, concerned the bride's appearance on her wedding day - perhaps she would wear borrowed jewellery from her mother or grandmother, a blue ribbon, or garter as it is today, an old piece of family lace and a new dress or pair of shoes.

This was one of many customs or superstitions surrounding the wedding day itself and the reception:

In the pit districts of Durham the bridal party were escorted to church by men armed with guns. These were fired again and again close to the ears of the bride and groom which *"terrified them sometimes not a little."*

The custom of throwing coins to waiting children at the church gate - *"Hoy a penny oot"* - although still carried out this century,

54

rarely takes place now. A variation on this was that the church gate would be locked until the groom paid a toll to enter.

A local custom in Whitburn, Sunderland was to send 'hot pots' to the church. As the couple left the ceremony women would hold out large mugs covered by a cloth which were passed to everyone to take a sip.

Winning the Kail

A country wedding was usually ended by a race for a ribbon, given by the bridegroom. When the race was over, winners and losers were entitled to a glass of spirits each and would arrive at the house to ask for their 'allowance'. A variation of this involved two or three wedding guests who dashed off on horseback and whoever was first to the groom's house was awarded the 'kail'. At one time this was a portion of spiced broth but in later years the winner received two ribbons, one which he fastened to the horse's bridle near the left ear, the other he attached to his coat. He would then set off to greet the approaching wedding party.

As the new bride arrived back at her home one of the oldest women in the village would be waiting on the doorstep to throw a plate of cake or shortbread over her head. A scramble among the unmarried girls then took place to retrieve a piece of cake to put under their pillows to ensure dreams of their sweethearts.

❖❖❖❖❖❖

Eating the posset

The wedding ring was dropped into a bowl containing a piece of white bread soaked in milk. The bride and groom ate first and the bowl was then passed around and whoever discovered the ring first would be next to marry.

The girl who received a piece of cheese cut by the bride before she left the reception table would be the next bride. After dinner the bride stuck her knife into the cheese and all the men at the table attempted to retrieve it and the one who succeeded without cutting his fingers in the struggle, ensured happiness in his married life. The knife was known as the 'best man's prize' and accordingly it was the 'best man' who obtained it, if not, his marriage prospects were doomed. The 'prize' for the girls was to obtain a piece of the wedding dress - 'a shaping' which was said to predict certain aspects concerning future husbands.

Throwing the stocking

After undressing on her wedding night, the bride gave one of her stockings to a bridesmaid who then threw it at random among the guests, the person on whom it landed was thought to be the next to be married. Another variation was that the guests were invited to the bride and groom's room where the couple removed their shoes and stockings. The bridesmaid took the groom's stocking and stood at the foot of the bed with her back towards it, throwing the stocking over her right shoulder with her left hand and aiming it at the groom's face. This was then done by all the unmarried females and anyone fortunate to hit the groom would soon be married herself. The bride's stocking was thrown in the same way by the men.

'ASHES TO ASHES'
Customs of death

".... the pulse ceases to play. The relatives and friends are gathered around, and the eyes are closed immediately after the breath is gone. When a period of about an hour has elapsed, the case containing feathers is drawn from above the mattress and put below the bed; the face and hands etc. are washed; the body is arrayed in dead-clothes; the arms are laid down by each side; the limbs are stretched out to their full length; and the whole frame is left to become stiff, rigid and cold as the earth in which it will soon be deposited.

The apartment is now arranged in a way suitable to the changes which have taken place. The bed is hung with white linen, the tables and drawers are covered with the same material; the looking-glass is also either covered or removed; a knot of white or black ribbon as the deceased was young or old is fastened to the head of the bed; and a white linen cloth is thrown over the body upon which is placed a plate containing a quantity of salt. All these offices are performed by female relatives and attendants, who like ministering angels are ever ready to yield us support and comfort in the hour of need: when we come into the world, they receive us; when we grow up and are laid upon a bed of sickness, they are there to tend and watch over us, and when at last death lays upon us his cold, icy hand, there are they still to put upon us our last dress, and place out limbs in a becoming position for the grave."

This graphic description taken from the *Local Historian's Table Book Legendary Vol.1*, gives us an idea of some of the customs and rituals which were concerned with death. Centuries ago, of course, when there were few hospitals or care centres most people died in their own homes and because of the lack of knowledge of scientific and medical matters, death was always surrounded with fear and superstition.

❖❖❖❖❖❖

Forewarnings of Death

Anyone who met a Border funeral was certain to die soon unless he bared his head and turned to accompany the procession for some distance. If the coffin was carried by bearers, then he must take his turn in the lifting. Having done this, if he bowed to the funeral party, he could go on his way without fear.

If the sun shone brightly on the face of an attendant at the funeral, this marked him as the next to be laid in the churchyard. If the sound of the 'mools' (clods of earth) falling on the coffin were heard by anyone some distance from the churchyard, there would be a death in that person's family.

In the Borders a crowing hen was regarded as the forerunner to death:

> *"A whistling woman and a crowing hen*
> *Are neither fit for God nor men."*

57

Other forewarnings of death included the sound of bells in the night, the chirping of crickets, circular lights seen in the air when there was no fire or candle, a call by day or night in the voice of an absent person, dogs howling at the door, hens laying eggs with double yolks, magpies flying around the house....

Three taps on a door or window by an unseen hand was also a warning of death. At Windy Walls, near Stamfordham, Northumberland, three such taps were heard on a window shutter and that same night a man who lived in the house accidentally fell from a cart and was killed.

After a death had taken place the straw from the bed of the deceased was taken to an open place and burned. The rest of the family looked for a footprint among the ashes and the member whose foot fitted the impression would be the next to die.

A mirror in the room where a death had taken place had to be removed or covered otherwise anyone who looked in it would see the corpse looking over their shoulder.

The Lyke Wake

A Lyke Wake was a constant vigil kept beside the deceased until their internment. The name derives from the Saxon lic- a body, and waecce - watch. The watchers worked a 'shift' system of sitting beside the body with refreshments supplied by helpful neighbours and friends. Although this was originally seen as a tribute to the dead, it was also open to abuse. Often it became an occasion for 'feasting and revelry' and instances are related of the corpse remaining unburied while the 'festivities' continued and the watchers consumed everything in the house. This was more likely to happen when the deceased lived alone.

Common Beliefs & Customs

In Sunderland an ancient custom, dating back to earliest times and observed until the late nineteenth century, was to decorate the deceased inside their coffins with wreaths of flowers. People used whatever flowers were in season and those with plentiful supplies in their gardens gave to their poorer neighbours.

So intense was the belief that it was ominous for a dog or a cat to pass over a coffin that the animal had to be killed. Two examples of this originate in Northumberland. Firstly, just as a funeral was leaving a house, a cat jumped over the coffin and no one would proceed until it was slaughtered. In the second instance, a funeral party was carrying a coffin from a lonely house on the fell and as the bearers put down their burden to pause for a rest, a sheep dog jumped over it. Without hesitation, everyone present decided that the dog should be killed before they went on.

It was customary to place a plate full of earth and salt on a corpse as an emblem of mortality and eternal life. Those who did not believe in these more mystical aspects of death, preferred to say that it prevented the body swelling as air was able to get into the bowels!

The Soul Bell

The tolling of a parish church bell at the time of a death or funeral, known as the passing bell or soul bell, was believed to drive out evil spirits. It was also the custom, first recorded by Bede, to summon people to pray for the soul of the dead:

'"When the bell begins to toll,
Lord have mercy on the soul."

A single stroke of the bell hammer signified the death of a child, two for a woman and three for a man.

In County Durham it was thought that the bodies of the drowned would float on the ninth day and that if a gun was fired over a dead body which was lying at the bottom of the sea or river, the concussion would break the gall bladder and cause the body to float.

A loaf of bread weighted with quick silver was floated on the water and was said to move over the place where a body had drowned. In 1860 a corpse was recovered from the River Wear, about 2 miles from Durham, using a loaf of bread and a lighted candle.

The friends of a young boy, Charles Colling, searched the river in vain after the child fell into the Wear near Shincliffe on 21st October 1860. Having tried conventional methods, they weighted a loaf with quick silver and floated it on the stream. Having watched it for some considerable time, it floated but failed to stop on the water over the child's resting place. The body was later recovered in the normal way.

"Life goes out with the tide, and comes in with it."

A common belief held along the east coast of England from Northumberland to Kent, was that deaths mostly occurred during an ebb tide. The following extract from a parish register of Hesildon, near Hartlepool, illustrates the importance which was placed on the turning of the tide:

"The xith daye of Maye A.D. 1595, at vi of ye clocke in the morninge, being full of water, Mr. Henrye Mitford of Hexham, died at Newcastle..."

Virgin's Garland

At one time it was the custom in country churches to hang a garland of artificial flowers, made from coloured paper, over the seats of deceased virgins as a token of esteem and love, and as their reward in the heavenly church. The various types of flowers were fastened to small sticks which crossed each other at the top and were fixed at the bottom with a circular hoop. A woman's glove was cut out in white paper, inscribed with the name and age of the deceased, and then suspended from the centre of the garland.

Also Published by Sandhill Press

AMBLE AND DISTRICT by T.L. McAndrews
First published in 1912, this book traces the history of the settlement from Celtic times to the beginning of this century.
Hardback £11.95 ISBN 0 946098 39 5

ANGLO SAXON NORTHUMBRIA by T.H. Rowland
Explores the Golden Age of Northumbria through this vivid account of a significant period in our history.
Paperback £2.99 ISBN 0 946098 34 4

BIGGEST MINING VILLAGE IN THE WORLD by Mike Kirkup
A social history of Ashington.
Paperback £9.95 ISBN 0 946098 30 1

THE BODY IN THE BANK: Famous Northern Murders
A fascinating collection of the murders, trials and subsequent harsh punishments which took place in our northern towns and countryside.
Paperback £1.95 ISBN 0 946098 33 6

BORDER LAND CASTLES AND PELES by Robert Hugill
First published in 1939, this book details over 100 strongholds on the Anglo Saxon border with a guide to places of interest.
Hardback £14.95 ISBN 0 946098 41 7

CUSTOMS AND TRADITIONS OF NORTHUMBRIA
Special ceremonies, seasons and times of the year.
Paperback £1.95 ISBN 0 946098 25 5

GHOSTS AND LEGENDS OF NORTHUMBRIA
2nd reprint of this collection of famous tales of ghosts, hauntings and strange happenings that form part of the folklore of Northumbria.
Paperback £2.50 ISBN 0 946098 44 1

THE GOLDEN AGE OF NORTHUMBRIA by Jane Hawkes
Depicts the splendours of the Anglo-Saxon kingdom of Northumbria.
Paperback £9.95 ISBN 0 946098 43 3

Also Published by Sandhill Press

THE GREAT GUNMAKER by David Dougan
A fascinating biography of the north's famous armaments manufacturer.
Paperback £6.95 ISBN 0 946098 23 9

HISTORY OF NORTHUMBERLAND by Cadwallader J. Bates
*Written and published in 1895 this is one of the standard histories referred
to frequently by writers, readers and lovers of the county.*
Hardback £16.95 0 946098 42 5

IN AND AROUND...Alnwick...Morpeth...Rothbury...Warkworth
by Ian Smith
Explores Northumberland's towns, villages & rivers. Maps & drawings.
Paperback £3.95 ISBN 0 946098 26 3

THE LAST YEARS OF A FRONTIER by D.L.W. Tough
A history of the Borders during the turbulent times of Elizabeth I.
Hardback £14.95 ISBN 0 946098 06 9

**MEDIEVAL CASTLES, TOWERS, PELES & BASTLES OF
NORTHUMBERLAND** by T.H. Rowland
*A reprint of this comprehensive guide to the many castles and Border
strongholds which form part of Northumbria's rich, often troubled history.*
Paperback £5.95 ISBN 0 946098 24 7

NORTHUMBERLAND PLACE NAMES: Goodwife Hot
by Godfrey Watson
*Starting with the Celts, the author traces the story behind hundreds of
place names up to the 19th century.*
Paperback £6.95 ISBN 0 946098 38 7

NORTHUMBRIA IN PICTURES by Beryl Sanderson
*A new revised edition of our successful souvenir guide-
40 superb colour photographs and accompanying text.*
Hardback £11.95 ISBN 0 946098 22 0